Thank you for a pair of jeans

Patricia & Victor Smeltzer

A LION BOOK

Jenny had a new pair of jeans.
for her birthday.

"Thank you, **Mummy,**
for my new jeans,"
said Jenny.

"Don't thank me,"
said Mummy.
"I only bought the jeans.
You must thank the one
who sold them to me."

So Jenny went to say
"Thank you" to ...

... the **shopkeeper.**

"Thank you, **shopkeeper,**
for my jeans,"
said Jenny.

"Don't thank me,"
said the shopkeeper.
"I only sold the jeans.
You must thank the one
who made them."

So Jenny went to say
"Thank you" to ...

... the **clothes factory workers.**

"Thank you,
clothes factory workers,
for my jeans," said Jenny.

"Don't thank us," said the workers.
"We only cut out
and sewed the jeans.
You must thank the one
who made the pattern for them."

So Jenny went to say
"Thank you" to ...

... the **clothes designer.**

"Thank you,
clothes designer,
for my jeans,"
said Jenny.

"Don't thank me,"
said the designer.
"I only made a pattern
to be cut from cloth.
You must thank the one
who made the cloth."

So Jenny went to say
"Thank you" to ...

... the **cotton mill workers.**

"Thank you,
cotton mill workers,
for my jeans," said Jenny.

"Don't thank us,"
said the workers.
"We only spun and wove
the cloth from cotton.
You must thank the ones
who brought us the raw cotton."

So Jenny went to say
"Thank you" to ...

... the **carriers.**

"Thank you, **carriers,**
for my jeans,"
said Jenny.

"Don't thank us,"
said the carriers.
"We only brought
the bales of raw cotton
to the mill.
You must thank the ones
who gave us the cotton."

So Jenny went to say
"Thank you" to ...

... the **cotton growers.**

"Thank you, **cotton growers,**
for my jeans,"
said Jenny.

"Don't thank us,"
said the growers.
"We only planted
and picked the cotton.
You must thank the ones who
grew into fluffy cotton bolls."

So Jenny went to say
"Thank you" to ...

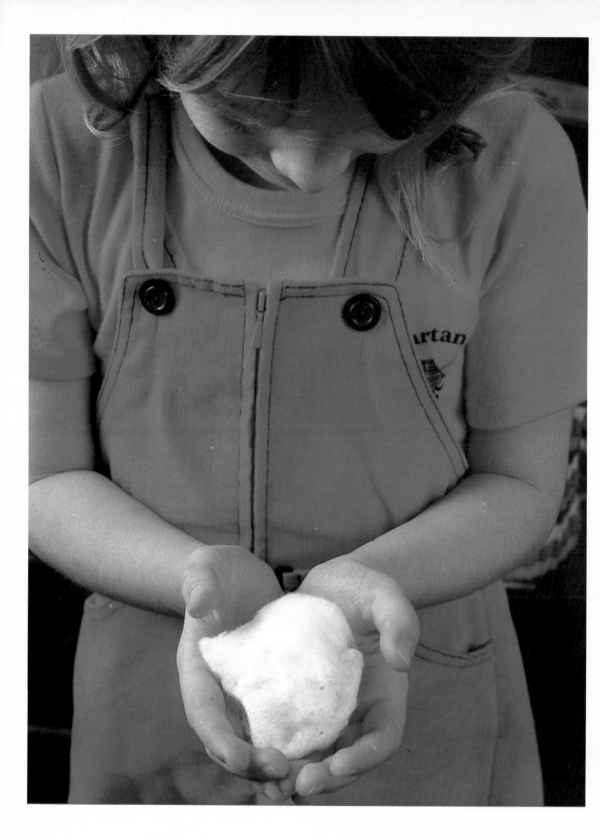

... the **cotton seeds.**

"Thank you, **cotton seeds,**
for my pair of jeans,"
said Jenny.

"Don't thank us,"
said the seeds.
"We needed other things
to help us grow.
You must thank them."

So Jenny went to say
"Thank you" to ...

... the **soil, rain** and **sun.**

"Thank you, **soil, rain** and **sun,**
for my jeans," said Jenny.

"Don't thank us,"
they all said.
"You must thank the one
who made us."

So Jenny said "Thank you" to ...

... God.

Jenny said this prayer:

"Thank you, **God,**
for making the
soil, rain and **sun;**

and for the
cotton seeds,

and for the
cotton grower.

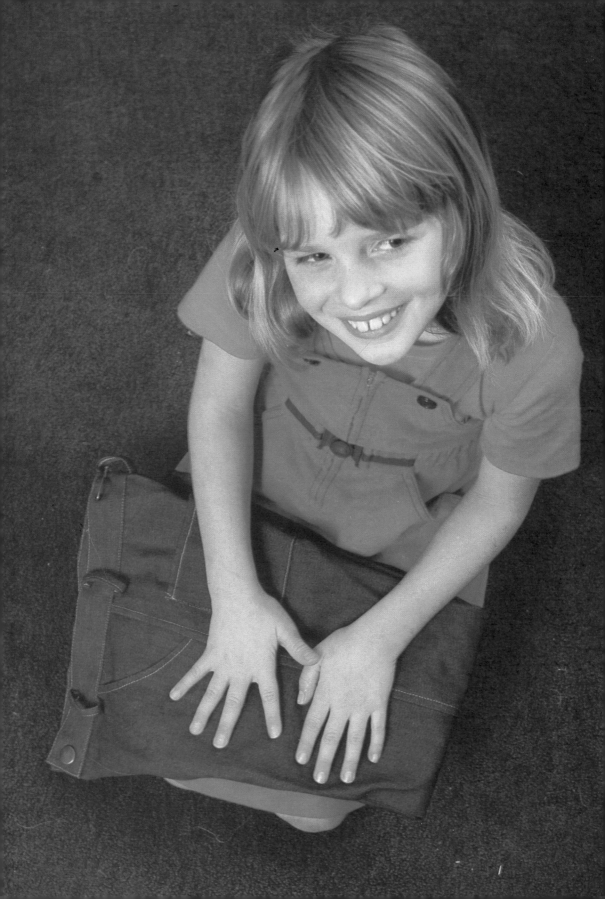

Thank you, **God,**
for the **carriers,**

and the **cotton mill workers;**

Thank you, **God,**
for the
clothes designer,

and for the **clothes factory workers,**

and for
the **shopkeeper**
who sold the jeans.

Thank you, **God,**
for my **Mummy**
who bought my new jeans.

Thank you
for my pair of jeans.

Amen."